Christopher Norton's

ESSENTIAL GUIDE TO LATIN STYLES

for keyboard

London · New York · Bonn · Sydney

Contents

Cover design by Sue Clarke
Cover photographs courtesy of Redferns Music Picture Library
Music set by Halstan & Co Ltd
Reproduced and printed by Halstan & Co Ltd,
Amersham, Bucks, England

INTRODUCTION

Latin American music is dance music from South and Central America, particularly Brazil, Cuba and the Caribbean islands. It is influenced by both European and African music, as will become clear in the course of this book. Most of the time, tempos are medium to fast (ranging from ♩ = 96 to ♩ =220!), though a few slow pieces are included to let you get your breath back.

Most Latin American music is based on a few basic styles. These have all been included in this book, as have some variations which demonstrate how a particular style can be altered to create a different mood.

The instrumentation in a Latin band tends to be:

- percussion (between 1 and 6 players)
- drum kit (but only in recent years - in "traditional" Latin bands, drum kit is not included)
- bass (upright or electric)
- piano
- guitar (electric and/or acoustic)
- 1 or 2 lead instruments, typically flute, trumpet, saxophone or guitar

The percussion section includes:

- claves
- cowbells (various pitches)
- timbales
- cabasa
- triangle
- guiro
- maracas and/or various shakers
- congas and/or bongos

If you don't have all the percussion instruments listed, you can improvise a Latin American percussion section - for claves, use woodblock; for timbales, use pots and pans; for cowbell, use a small saucepan; for guiro, use a washboard scraped with a knitting needle.

Latin American music should above all be fun to play. Look around for potential instruments - if it makes a good sound, use it! Every kitchen or garage contains a potential Latin percussion section (but don't use the best pressure cooker!)

About learning Latin rhythms

When learning a new style, it is important to be able to subdivide the beat. Learn to think ♩♩ , then ♩♩♩♩ , then ♫♫ , then 𝅘𝅥𝅯𝅘𝅥𝅯𝅘𝅥𝅯 𝅘𝅥𝅯𝅘𝅥𝅯𝅘𝅥𝅯 𝅘𝅥𝅯𝅘𝅥𝅯𝅘𝅥𝅯 𝅘𝅥𝅯𝅘𝅥𝅯𝅘𝅥𝅯 . You should be able to accent any note in the bar, particularly ♪ note values. Up-tempo Latin music is often notated in 2/2 or ¢, but for the purposes of this book, 4/4 has been used. This makes some of the notation easier to read.

The most distinctive feature of Latin American music is the clave rhythm. There are two common patterns, one consisting of 3 notes then 2 notes (called a 3:2 pattern), and the other of 2 notes followed by 3 notes (a 2:3 pattern). This is what they look like:

3:2: $\frac{4}{4}$ 𝅘𝅥. 𝅘𝅥𝅮𝄾 𝅘𝅥 | 𝄾 𝅘𝅥 𝅘𝅥 𝄾 :‖

2:3: $\frac{4}{4}$ 𝄾 𝅘𝅥 𝅘𝅥 𝄾 | 𝅘𝅥. 𝅘𝅥𝅮𝄾 𝅘𝅥 :‖

If you can play either of these rhythms on claves over a steady 4/4 ♩ beat (either tap your foot or ask someone else to keep time), you are getting into the right frame of mind.

When you hear them at first, Latin rhythms can seem complicated, but in fact they are often made up of different layers of percussion parts. If you listen closely, it soon becomes easier to hear what each part is playing. The explanatory notes on each style concentrate on percussion, drums and bass parts, as so many of the styles are all about rhythm and accents. In the conga parts, "+" denotes a closed sound, ">" a slap sound, and "o" an open sound. In the triangle parts, "+" denotes a stopped sound, "o" an open sound; in the guiro parts, the arrows indicate the direction of the scraper. If you can play any one of the rhythm patterns suggested along with the piano part, you are already gaining valuable insights into how it feels to play Latin American styles.

Christopher Norton, Leeds, UK, January 1996

1 · Afro-rock

This is a very relaxed style, characterised by the  piano figure played against a strict-time backing. The improvisatory nature of the melody is nicely balanced with the more ordered elements of the accompaniment.

The clave pattern looks like this:

This is called the 3:2 son clave pattern (3 notes in bar 1, 2 notes in bar 2) and is the cornerstone of many Latin styles.

Once you have mastered the clave pattern, try adding the cowbell pattern to it:

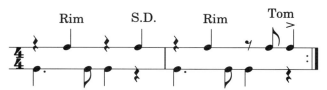

You will see at once how important it is to learn to sub-divide the beat! Together with the triplets in the piano melody, these two percussion parts create the distinctive Afro-Rock effect.

The bass and drums are very "straight" in this style - the drums tend to put accents on the last beat of a 2-bar pattern:

and the bass is on the beat:

A general comment is that, at any given time, someone in the percussion section is playing ♪ patterns, though the individual parts are more of a combination of ♪ and ♪ patterns. Try improvising various patterns on percussion, bringing one player in at a time, and see if you can keep ♪ patterns going all the time - if you're playing ♫ , someone else can play ♬♬ . But listen to each other and try not to let things get too busy or cluttered, especially in a piece at this tempo.

Examples: Santana: *Black Magic Woman*
Santana: *Oye Como Va*
Celine Dion: *Falling Into You*

2 · Beguine

This style is relatively relaxed and unhurried, with on-beat bass and bass drum parts. The main rhythmic feel is a combination of ♩ ♩ ♩ in the bass and bass drum, and off-beats on snare drum and piano. The melody of this piece is a melancholy, minor-key example, but major-key beguines are not uncommon. The style lends itself to many moods - many melodies can be given the beguine treatment.

The clave pattern is 3:2:

Once you have this going, add a straight ♪ pattern on maracas:

Add this part for two bongos:

The snare drum has a characteristic pattern, which should be played with a light feel:

The bass and bass drum play relatively "straight" patterns throughout:

Examples: Consuelo Velasquez: *Besame Mucho*
Alberto Velasquez: *Frenesi*
Cole Porter: *Begin the Beguine*

3 · Bolero

This style is related to the beguine, but it is a type of ballad, usually performed by a vocalist. Claves play the 3:2 pattern again:

Patterns for shaker and bongos should be played with very even strokes:

The emphasis is on even ♩♩♩♩ – try playing shaker and bongos with the piano part.

If you don't have a percussion section, play ♩♩♩♩ ♩♩♩♩ on hi-hat, the clave pattern on rim, and ♩ ♩ ♩ on bass drum.

The important accents in many Latin styles can be played by various instruments in the percussion department. The most important aspect is where the accents fall, not necessarily which instrument plays them. So you can try some of the patterns given on instruments other than the ones suggested and see which variations you prefer.

Note the "throbbing", off-beat piano accompaniment. The root note of A shifting downward chromatically is very characteristic of this style. The melody has an almost improvisatory feel, while the accompaniment is in strict time. This combination of order and freedom is distinctively Latin.

Examples: Rafael Hernandez: *Lamento Borincano*
Tito Puente: *Stella by Starlight* (from the album "El Rey")

4 · Bossa Nova

Cabasa, triangle and maracas are the appropriate instruments for this style, because of their lighter pitch and tonal quality. Hand-drums (e.g. congas and bongos) would not be used.

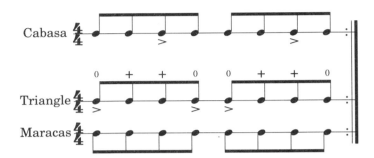

Bass drum and bass play this very distinctive pattern throughout:

Hi-hats play even ♫, with occasional open hi-hats. Rim-shot plays this variation of the clave pattern:

The piano plays inversions in the left hand, leaving root notes to the bass. In the middle section, a "locked-hand" style is used, with both hands playing the same chords two octaves apart. In any gaps in the melody, a solo instrument such as guitar or flute can improvise a "fill".

Examples:　Antonio Carlos Jobim: *The Girl from Ipanema*
　　　　　　Antonio Carlos Jobim: *Desafinado*

5 · Calypso 1

The most characteristic calypso rhythm is:

Try clapping this pattern against tapped ♩ beats.

The claves play the basic rhythm. Other percussion instruments play variations of the original rhythm, always keeping the distinctive accent in mind. Maracas play straight ♫♫. Congas also emphasize ♪, playing:

The cowbell offsets the main accent:

Try getting one person to clap the pattern at the top of this page and another to clap the cowbell pattern. Once you can do this, add in the conga pattern, also clapped. Then add guiro on the off-beats:

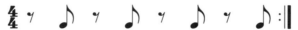

The bass drum also plays the main rhythm, emphasising the fourth ♪ of each group. Note the "straight" hi-hat pattern:

This piece is fast and extrovert, in a major key and using primary chords only. It is ideal for getting used to chord changes on piano, keyboard or guitar while percussion parts are being played. Flute, trumpet and trombone are likely lead instruments. You could also try the piece with timbales playing "paila" style on the sides of the shell:

Try using an acoustic guitar in this tune, strummed energetically throughout with a full-bodied sound.

Example: Harry Belafonte: *Banana Boat Song*

6 · Calypso 2

This is another extrovert, happy piece with simple chords in the first section and unison lines 2 octaves apart in the second. Here is the clave pattern:

The cowbell plays the same pattern as Calypso 1:

Other percussion parts are in a mixture of ♪ rhythms, with congas in particular emphasising:

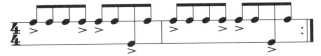

The drums are similar to "Calypso 1":

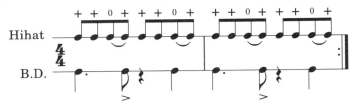

and cabasa and guiro heighten the effect:

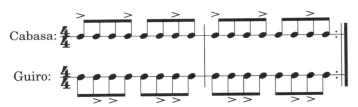

To add excitement, timbales can play fills at the ends of phrases, but be careful not to overdo this. The timbale player can improvise patterns on the side of the stand or the shell of the drum, using thin sticks if possible.

Bass guitar locks in with bass drum and typically plays tonic, 3rd, and 5th of each chord:

The piano left hand also plays this pattern.

Example: Sonny Rollins: *St Thomas*

7 · Cha cha 1

Traditionally, there is no clave pattern in a cha cha, but many bands do use it. In this example, the claves play a 2:3 pattern:

Clap this rhythm, with a ♩ beat from your foot. Now try it on claves and add the guiro pattern:

There are no very strong accents in the percussion, although there is a strong 4/4 feeling (put slight accents on each ♩ beat).

Cowbell can play:

Here is the conga pattern:

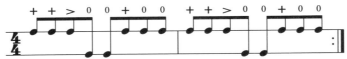

The hihat emphasises the same "straight" rhythm as the guiro, but only if no guiro is available. Don't use both at the same time:

The following rhythm is played on the bass drum and snare drum, with an optional tom part. Use the tom if no congas are available.

The bass plays variations on this characteristic line:

The second section has unison melody lines with the percussion building in excitement to a classic cha cha ending.

Examples: Vincent Youmans: *Tea for Two*
Alberto Dominguez: *Frenesi*

8 · Cha cha 2

Claves play a 3:2 pattern in this piece:

The clave plays 2:3 in Cha cha 1 and 3:2 in Cha cha 2; which pattern you use depends on the shape of the melody.

Once again, the guiro plays a "straight" role:

This pattern is very common in Latin music.

Cowbell plays on the beat again:

Bongos play this pattern (again, relatively unaccented):

Here are the drum parts:

The rim plays quietly, and the ♫ on the 4th beat of the bar are emphasised by toms (in the absence of bongos). The drums play a fairly straight role - they need to, as the bass is off the beat for much of the piece. The bass 2-bar pattern looks like this:

etc.

The second section contains the typical ♩♩♩ "loose" melodic style combined with metronomic backing. Note the traditional "cha cha cha" ending.

Examples: Juan Tizol: *Perdido*
Dizzy Gillespie: *Guarachi Guaro*
Howard Schneider: *La Cuna*

9 · Conga

The basic conga rhythm is:

Virtually all instruments aim to hit the ♪ accent (which is called a "bombo" beat).

Claves play a 2:3 pattern:

Cabasa helps hold things together with an unaccented pattern:

The cowbell pattern:

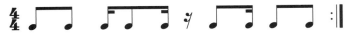

Even the bass drum hits the main accent, with rhythmic toms creating an earthy effect:

The rest of the percussion should play inventive variations of:

The bass, thankfully, sticks to the same rhythm pattern as the bass drum, which should make the whole effect very solid.

The main melody and chords play the same basic rhythm, more or less.

Examples: James Cavanaugh: *I Came, I Saw, I Conga'd*
Gloria Estefan: *Conga*
Josephine Baker: *Conga Biloti*

10 · Guaracha

This style is usually fairly bright in mood and tempo and this piece is no exception. Think of it as 2 in a bar.

Just for a change, the claves play a 3:3 pattern:

This gives a sense of urgency but doesn't clutter up the rhythm, enabling other percussion instruments to be a bit freer.

Maracas play a straight pattern:

Congas play the following:

Add cowbell:

Put all these elements with the piano, and the Guaracha style is already fully in evidence.

The bass plays the most syncopated part we have yet encountered:

Try not to play this part too heavily, and link it in with the bass drum.

Examples: Guillermo Rodríguez Fiffé: *Bilongo*
Rafael Hernández: *Cachita*
Noro Morales: *María Cervantes*

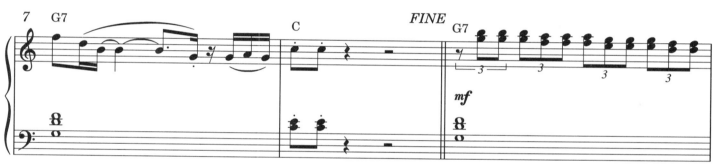

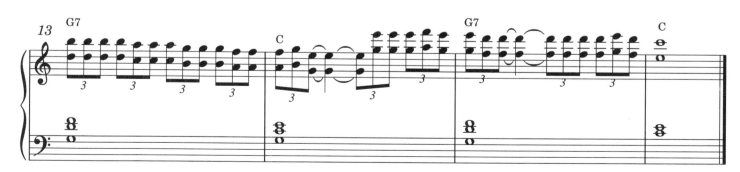

D.C. al Fine

11 · Mambo 1

This tends to be a very lively style. Claves play a 2:3 pattern:

Guiro plays its usual straight pattern:

Cowbell leans on the first beat of the bar, in this relatively agile pattern:

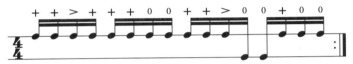

Congas play this pattern:

Drum kit plays lightly - the bass drum plays a similar pattern to the guaracha bass drum, but more syncopated. If all the percussion is available, the kit player should play ♫♫ on hihat and the bass drum part as indicated:

Hihat
B.D.

As you can see, the bass part is entirely off the beat, without even a downbeat to help out!

Examples: Duke Ellington: *Caravan*
Perez Prado: *Mambo Jambo*

12 · Mambo 2

This is similar to Mambo 1, but there are some subtle differences in the percussion.

Claves play 3:2:

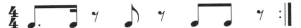

Guiro plays the same pattern as in Mambo 1:

The pattern the cowbell plays is called *cascara*. It is frequently found in Latin styles.

Congas, as usual, are slightly more complicated:

As in Mambo I, play ♫♫ on hihat, nothing at all on snare, and an even sparer bass drum pattern:

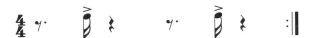

The tune alternates unison and octaves plus thirds very effectively.

Examples: Kennedy/Carr: *South of the Border*
 Tito Puente: *Para los rumberos*

D.C. al Fine (with repeat)

13·Merengue

Merengue feels as if it is 2 in a bar.

Claves play 3:2:

Guiro plays:

Cowbell plays:

Bongos and congas fit together very effectively:

Note that they both emphasize the ♪♪♪♪ pattern on beat 4.

The bass drum of the kit is on the beat, and the hihats play accented ♪ patterns.

The bass is the "oom-pa" man in this piece, playing straight ♩♩♩♩ throughout.

Example: Luis Kaláff: *Compadre Pedro Juan*

14 · Mozambique 1

A 2:3 clave pattern:

Cowbell plays:

Congas play:

Notice where the accents in the piece are - these define the Mozambique style. The left hand of the piano reinforces the first accent.

Drums also reinforce the characteristic Mozambique accent:

The bass pattern for this piece is very syncopated, emphasizing nearly all the accents everyone else is trying to play!

Mozambique as a style is related to Mambo and Son Montuno, and is rather jolly and light-hearted. This piece is in a major key, with quite adventurous chord progressions in the second section.

Example: Paul Simon: *Late in the Evening*

15 · Mozambique 2

The clave pattern for this piece is called a rumba clave:

The pattern below is for cowbell. Try clapping it while tapping a steady ♩ beat with your foot. (Keep reminding yourself where you are in relation to a pulse and keep sub-dividing!) It is best to learn it a bit at a time. First of all:

a)

then

b)

then

c)

and finally

d)

The congas play the same pattern as in Mozambique 1:

Work all these parts up slowly so that claves, cowbell and congas feel totally "meshed". It should then be easy to add the hi-hat:

Finally, bass drum:

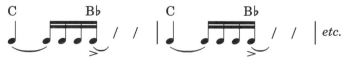

Now you are ready to add the piano. If you want to practise the chord changes in the first section, the cowbell ♪ is emphasised:

| C | | Bb | | C | | Bb | |

etc.

The bass really jumps around in this piece, cheerfully influenced by any or all of the percussion.

Example: Sergio Mendes: *Mas que nada*

♩ = 106
On repeats 8 ad lib.
C
B♭
to Coda
f
C
B♭
Fsus
F
F
E♭
mf
mp
D♭
B
cresc.
Coda
gliss.
ff
D.C. al Coda (with repeat)

16 · Nanigo

In this style, 3/4 and 6/8 are continually in tension.

Here is a percussion score:

Now add congas:

When you hear the individual parts, they sound simple. When heard in context all together, the effect is surprisingly complex.

A large floor tom on the beat is a very effective, almost folkloric addition:

Claves don't play a 2:3 or 3:2 pattern, but the cowbell part is similar to the rumba clave.

In the absence of full percussion, the drum kit can cover most of the basic feel:

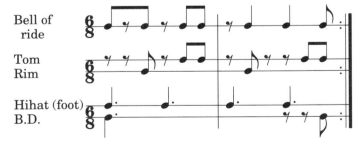

The bass alternates 3/4 and 6/8

Example: Mongo Santamaria: *Afro Blue*

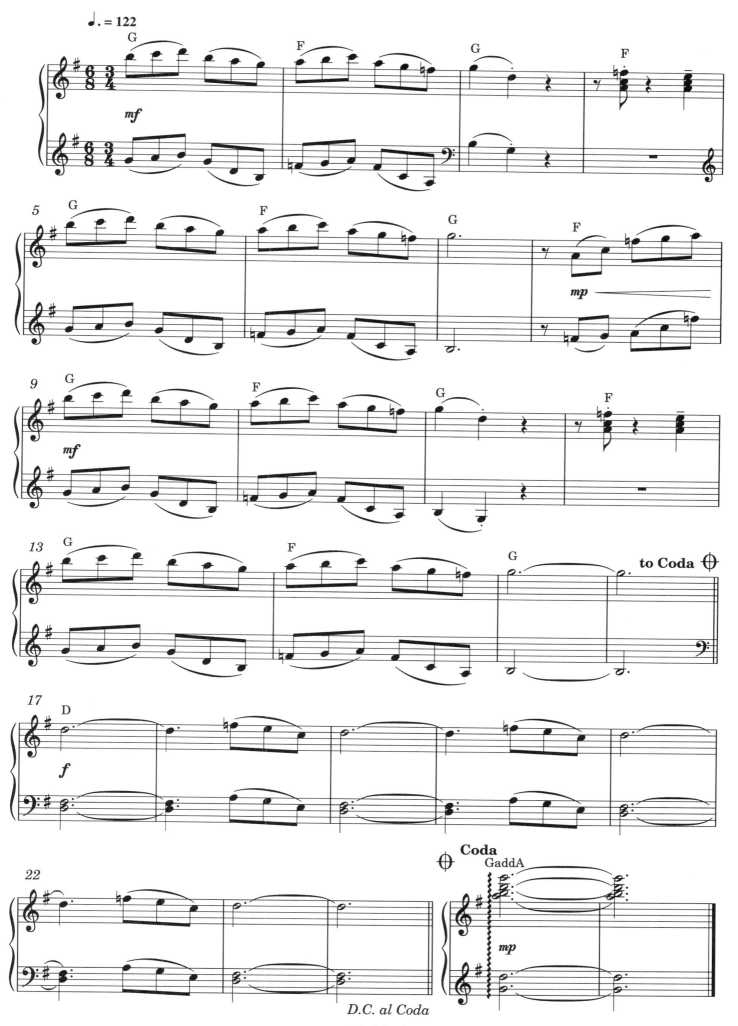

17 · Pachanga 1

This features bass "tumbao" (a bass and conga pattern). Try tapping this exercise - the "tumbao" rhythm is in the left hand:

Percussion is fairly straightforward, led by cowbell:

Here is the clave pattern:

Congas play a classic pattern:

If you use a drum kit (instead of, rather than as well as, the percussion parts) here is a score:

The bass part is a typical "tumbao" common to most Afro-Cuban music:

Try to work out a bass part for the rest of the piece!

Example: Gloria Estefan: *Vaya con Dios*

18 · Pachanga 2

This has the same basic elements as Pachanga 1, but is quicker in tempo and includes syncopations ideally suited to punctuations by the baritone sax:

A 3:2 clave pattern:

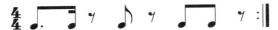

Cowbell plays a slightly simpler part than in Pachanga 1. Note the accents:

Congas play the same pattern as in Pachanga 1:

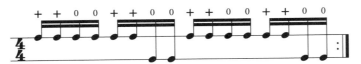

In the second section, shaker plays the same pattern as congas.

Again, if drum kit is used, omit the percussion (and vice versa). Here is the kit score:

The bass plays a similar "tumbao" figure to that in Pachanga 1:

Allow the piano to introduce the theme over percussion only for 8 bars before bass and drums join in. You can repeat this piece with minimal accompaniment from percussion or with the full band - the style is all about the accents.

Example: Arturo Sandoval: *La Guarapachanga*

19 · Rumba 1

Rumba is another style where the bass part is very off-beat.

Use the rumba clave pattern:

The guiro part is very lively:

Cowbell plays a cascara pattern. Note the accents:

Congas play:

Maracas or shaker play:

The bass is very syncopated (the "tumbao" pattern again):

The characteristic accents are also caught by the piano.

Examples: Enric Madriguera: *Adios*
Gabriel Ruiz: *Amor*

20 · Rumba 2

The percussion parts in this piece are the same as in Rumba 1.

A drum kit is not usually used in a traditional rumba, but it can be added as long as the playing is musical and tasteful. Here are the kit parts for this piece:

Try tapping the hihat pattern with your right hand, and ♩ ♩ ♩ ♩ with your left. Then try the same thing with the snare and bass drum patterns.

If you have a limited amount of percussion available, use claves and guiro with the kit as a minimum.

The bass is the same pattern as rumba 1, with a gap on beat 1:

In the middle section the bass drops out and a close harmony riff is repeated that builds in intensity, with exuberant percussion fills in the short gaps between phrases.

Examples: Earle Hagan: *Harlem Nocturne*
Ray Noble: *Lady of Spain*

21 · Samba

This style is related to the bossa nova, but tends to be quicker in tempo. You need to think and feel in 2 rather than in 4 (as in the bossa nova). The bass part and bass drum part are the same as the bossa nova, but try to accent the 3rd beat of the bar, which helps to give a feeling of 2:

The cabasa part is accented:

If you have ago-go bells, try this pattern:

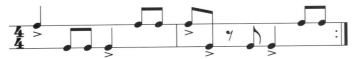

The basic drum kit part - this should have a light feel:

A variation would be to play the ride cymbal part on closed hi-hat and add triangle:

Examples: Peggy Lee: *Manana*
Al Jarreau: *Agua de beber*

22 · Songo 1

Being a fairly recent style (developed in the 1970s), this is ideal for drum kit. It is influenced by rock and funk from the USA, as well as by Caribbean styles.

Claves play 2:3

The cowbell part:

Now add guiro:

Try all the above with the piano before adding the drum kit.

Now the kit parts:

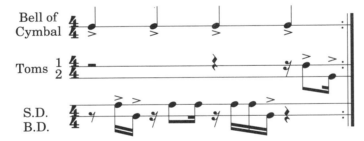

The bass is very syncopated, but on this occasion there is a downbeat on beat 1:

Example: Juan Formell: *Guararé*

23 · Songo 2

In many Latin styles, once a rhythmic groove has been established, a number of different harmonic elements can be used. These can range from single notes through a few simple primary chords to the most complicated jazz harmonies. In this example, unison is a feature of the first section, with very simple chords in the re-statement. Compare this with the rich harmonies of Songo 1.

This piece borrows more from the Caribbean in terms of melody and harmony than from the USA.

The percussion score:

Now add the kit parts from Songo 1:

Bass (starting at bar 9) is the same as Songo 1, but with the first beat of the bar silent:

Example: Arturo Sandoval: *Groovin' High*

24 · Son Montuno

This is a traditional Latin style. It has links with the cha cha.

Claves play a 3:2 pattern:

Guiro plays the standard pattern:

Cowbell plays the same pattern as the guiro, but with accents added:

The conga parts:

If the drum kit is used, keep claves and cowbell, even guiro. Here are the drum parts:

Now that a solid rhythmic groove has been created, the bass can be very syncopated. The notes are simple enough, but the rhythm is the most complex yet:

This piece shows how stops and fills can be used to dramatic effect. Notice the use of jazz inversions in the piano left hand.

Examples: Chano Pozo: *Por qué tu sufres?*
                 Adolfo Peñalver: *Báilala pronto*
                 Arsenio Rodriques: *Dame un cachito pá huelé*

KEYBOARD MUSIC
by Christopher Norton

LAVENDER'S KIND OF BLUE · Seven piano inventions on nursery rhymes, for grown-ups. *8176*

COCKTAIL LOUNGE · These Foolish Things, Jamaican Rumba and many other favourites arranged for piano. *7758*

ROCK PRELUDES · Seven preludes based on the strong rhythms of rock music. Equally effective played separately or as a suite – ideal as concert items. *8181*

LATIN PRELUDES · Seven preludes based on a variety of Latin American styles, including the samba, beguine and bossa nova. Great fun for the more experienced player. *8344*

LATIN PRELUDES CASSETTE · *8450*

20TH CENTURY CLASSICS VOLUMES ONE AND TWO · Well-loved themes from some of this century's favourite composers, including Rachmaninoff, Copland, Prokofieff, Holst and Britten. *8103, 8106.*
Also available: **20TH CENTURY CLASSICS FOR PIANO DUET.** *8478*

SWING A CAROL · Seven improvisations on well-known Christmas carols. *8477*

LAVENDER'S KIND OF BLUE · Sieben Klavier-inventionen auf Kinderreime für Erwachsene. *8176*

COCKTAIL LOUNGE · These Foolish Things, Jamaican Rumba und viele andere beliebte Melodien, für Klavier bearbeitet. *7758*

ROCK PRELUDES · Sieben Präludien auf der Grundlage der harten Rhythmen des Rock. Als separate Konzertstücke ebenso wirkungsvoll zu spielen wie als Suite. *8181*

LATIN PRELUDES · Sieben Präludien auf der Grundlage einer Vielzahl von südamerikanischen Stilen einschl. Samba, Beguine und Bossa nova. Ein Vernügen für den schon etwas erfahreneren Pianisten. *8344*

LATIN PRELUDES KASSETTE · *8450*

20TH CENTURY CLASSICS Bände 1 und 2 · Beliebte Themen von einigen der bekannten Komponisten dieses Jahrhunderts, u.a. Rachmaninoff, Copland, Prokofieff, Holst und Britten. *8103, 8106.*
Auch erhältlich: **20TH CENTURY CLASSICS** für Klavier zu vier Händen. *8478*

SWING A CAROL · Sieben Improvisationen zu bekannten Weihnachtsliedern. *8477*

LAVENDER'S KIND OF BLUE · A l'usage des adultes: sept inventions pour piano sur des comptines. *8176*

COCKTAIL LOUNGE · These Foolish Things, Jamaican Rumba et autres morceaux de prédilection arrangés pour piano. *7758*

ROCK PRELUDES · Sept préludes aux rythmes forts empruntés à la musique rock. Produisent autant d'effet en exécution individuelle qu'en continu. Parfaits comme morceaux de concert. *8181*

LATIN PRELUDES · Divers styles latin-américain – samba, beguine et bossa nova y compris – ont inspiré ces sept préludes. Ils feront la joie des joueurs exercés. *8344*

LATIN PRELUDES CASSETTE · *8450*

20TH CENTURY CLASSICS volume un et deux · Thèmes favoris de quelques-uns des compositeurs préférés de ce siècle: Rachmaninoff, Copland, Prokofieff, Holst et Britten, parmi d'autres. *8103, 8106.* Est aussi disponible: **20TH CENTURY CLASSICS** pour duos pour piano. *8478*

SWING A CAROL · Sept improvisations sur des noëls connus. *8477*

BOOSEY & HAWKES

Boosey & Hawkes Music Publishers Limited
295 Regent Street, London W1R 8JH

Ad.151